# 300
## DRAWING
## PROMPTS

D1176882

© 2016 Piccadilly (USA) Inc.

This edition published by Piccadilly (USA) Inc.

Piccadilly (USA) Inc.
12702 Via Cortina, Suite 203
Del Mar, CA 92014
USA

All rights reserved. No part of this publication may be reproduced, stored in a retrieval system,
or transmitted in any form or by any means, electronic, mechanical, photocopying, recording,
or otherwise, without prior consent of the publisher.

10  9  8  7  6  5  4  3  2  1

Printed in China

ISBN-13: 978-1-62009-851-6

Angel's wings

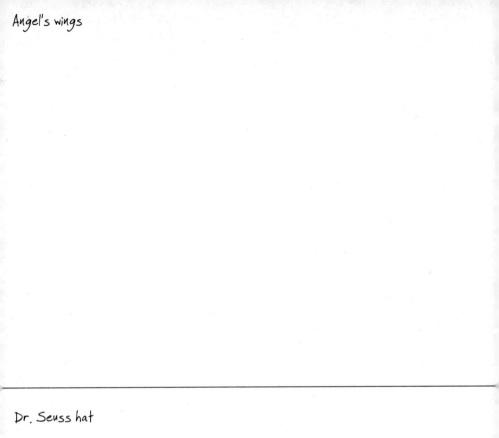

Dr. Seuss hat

Your reflection

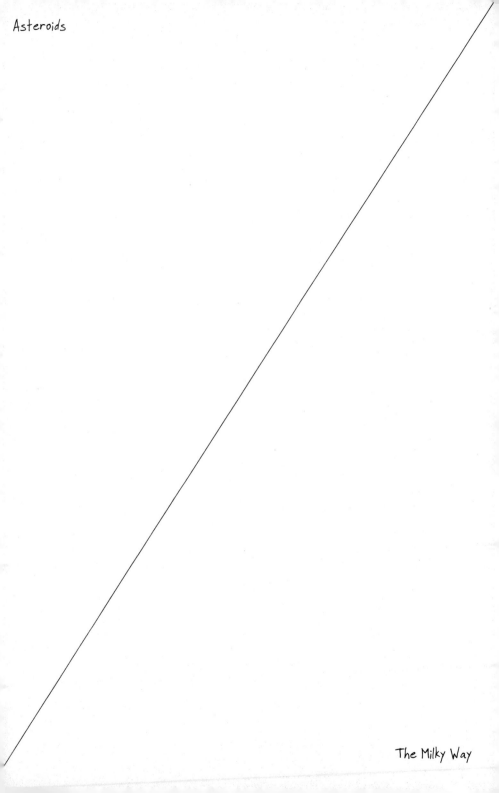

Asteroids

The Milky Way

Comic book cover

Lotus flower

---

Looking through a keyhole

Tree of life

Something with two heads

| Light saber | Grim Reaper |
| --- | --- |

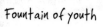
Fountain of youth

Man in the moon

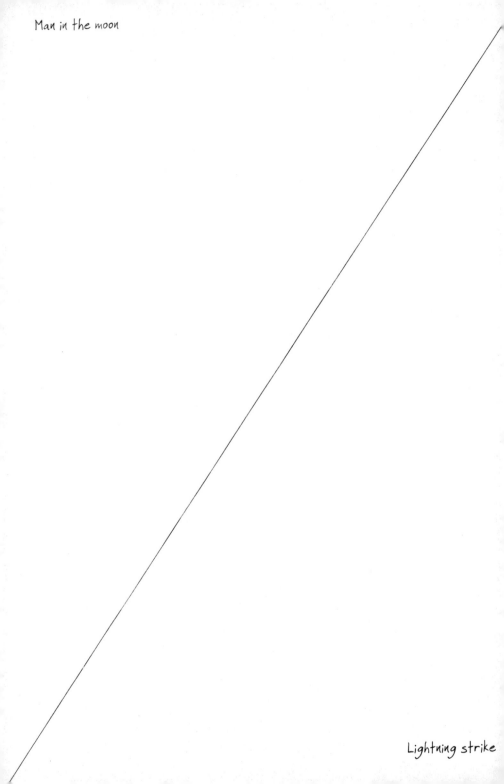

Lightning strike

Goddess

Psychedelic portal

A view from the top

Masquerade mask

Poseidon

Jackal

---

Deer antlers

Medusa

Carousel

Voodoo doll

Tiki idol

Sugar skull

Something abstract

Aladdin's lamp

---

Tooth fairy

Blue prints

| Cyborg | Totem pole |
| --- | --- |

Magic kingdom

Beach scene

Pac-Man video game

---

Your zodiac sign

Something 3-D

Anaconda

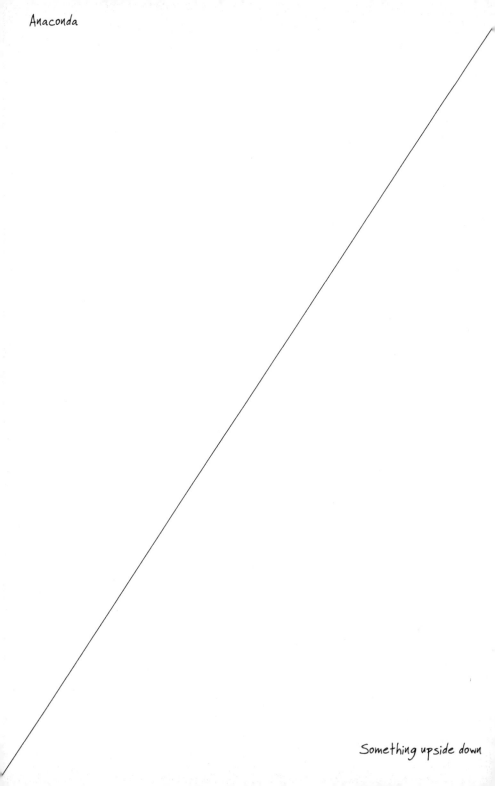

Something upside down

Computer from the future

---

A bright idea

Grand Canyon

Lion

Mad Hatter

Football

Dollar bill

Koala bear

Hummingbird

Woolly mammoth

Giraffe | Wishing well

Bull's-eye

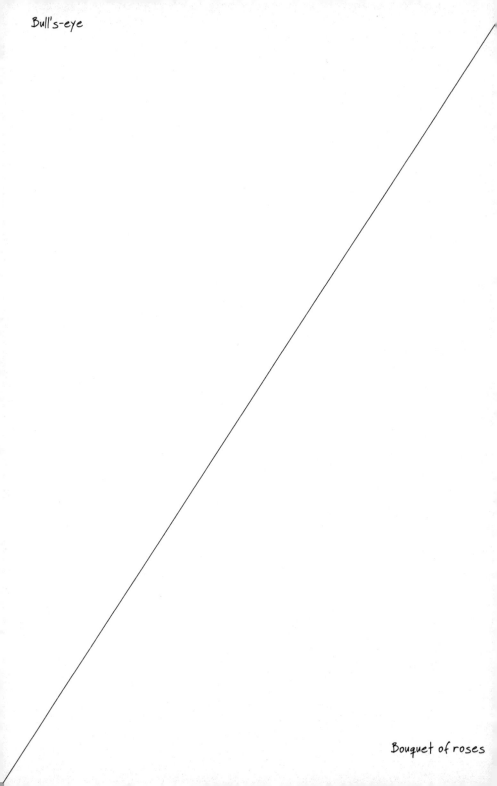

Bouquet of roses

Aurora borealis sky

Boombox

Ticket stub

Captain's hat

Something nautical

Banjo

Bowling alley & pins

Labyrinth

The Kraken

Armadillo

Eiffel Tower

Jack-in-the-box

Goblet

Mutant

Weeping willows

---

Grappling hook

Shepherd

---

Your country's flag

Water slide

Didgeridoo

Power lines

Olympic medals

Warrior

Stop sign

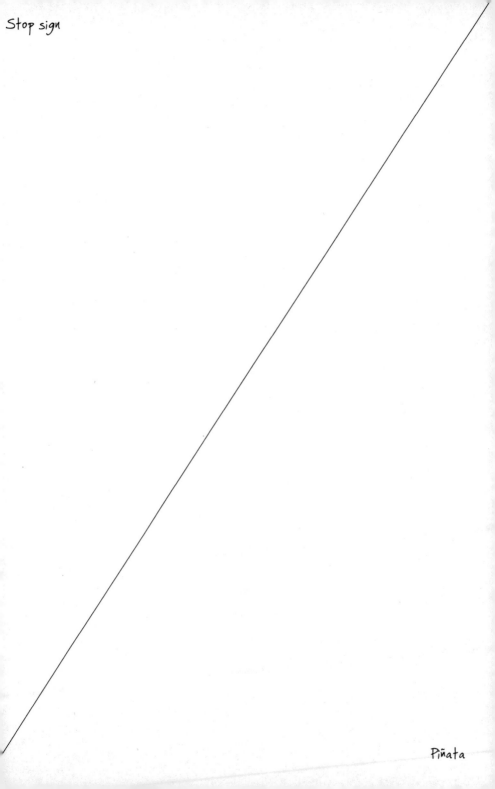

Piñata

Colosseum

Artichoke

---

Bushel of carrots

Bubbling cauldron

Crystal ball

Alphabet soup

Rubber ducky in a bubble bath

Red Riding Hood

Flamingo

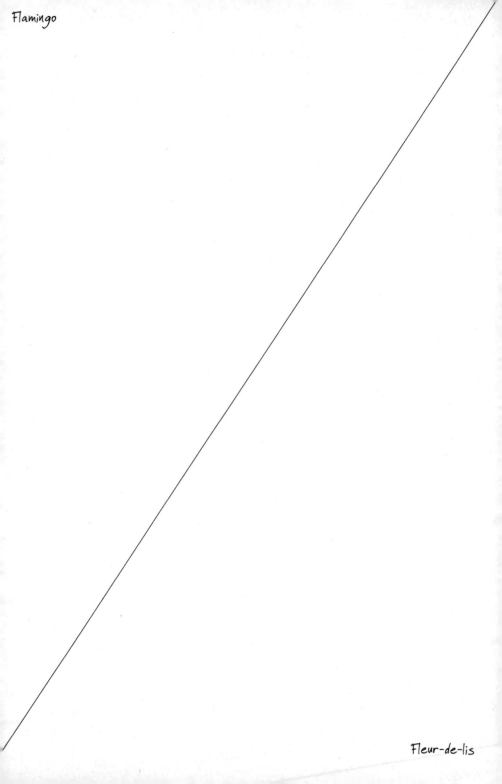

Fleur-de-lis

Noah's Ark

Lit candle | Hourglass

Three Blind Mice

Honeycomb

Compass

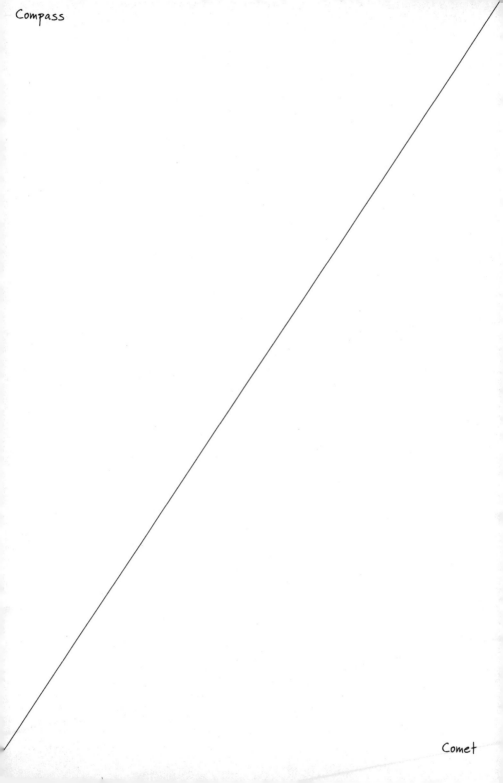

Comet

Snow globe

Stonehenge

Your school mascot

Racetrack

Jungle

Lily pad with frog

---

Your favorite emoji

Hologram

Robot

Hawaiian lei

---

North Pole

Rainforest

Gecko

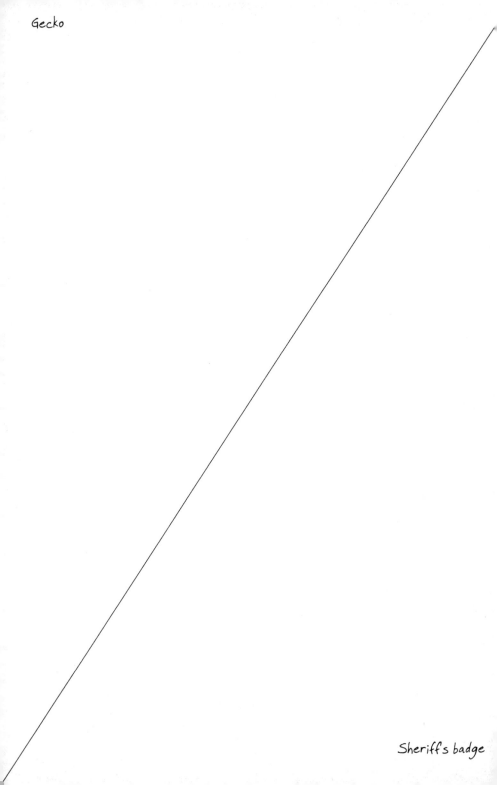

Sheriff's badge

Grandfather clock

Tribal spear

Sundial

---

Eggs frying in a skillet

Gingerbread man

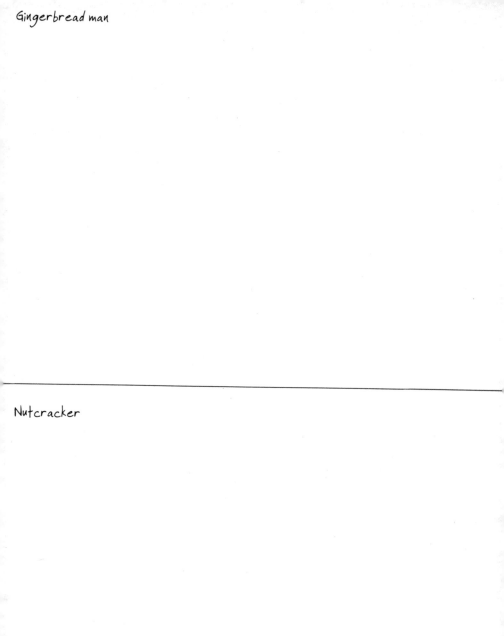

Nutcracker

When pigs fly

Tacos

---

Bowl of macaroni and cheese

Your favorite superhero

Castle

Talking parrot

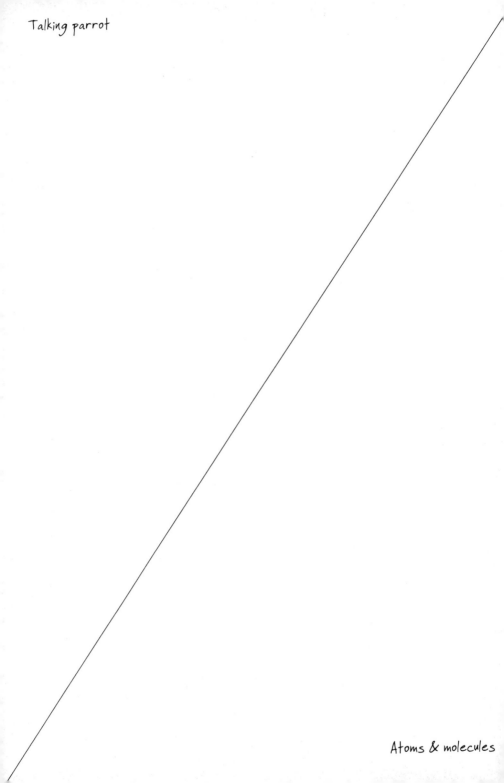

Atoms & molecules

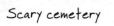
Scary cemetery

Stained glass window

Personalized license plate

Charm bracelet

Skyscraper

Sorcerer's wand

Field of sunflowers

Abandoned ghost town

Cool mailbox

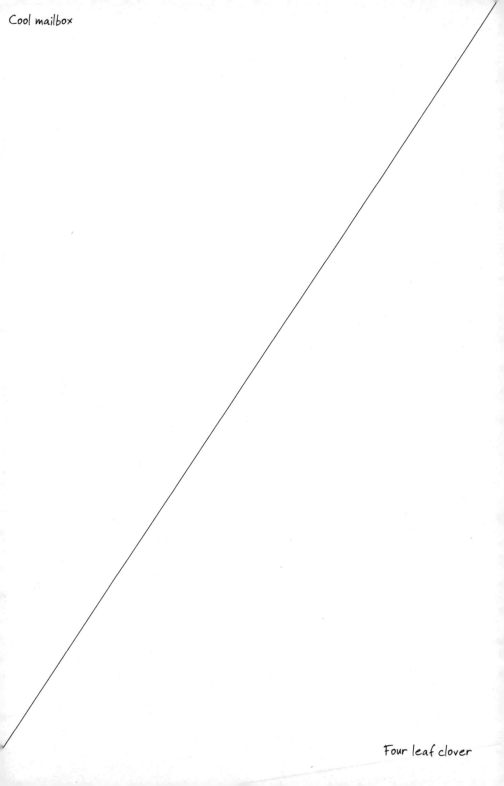

Four leaf clover

Angel

Monkeys

Bumper sticker

---

Hammock

Garden gnome

Good vs Evil

Peeled orange

Pomegranate center

Giant moth

| Snowflakes | Parachute |
| --- | --- |

Frankenstein

Science experiment

All seeing eye

Roller coaster

Your favorite cartoon

Kangaroo

Donut with sprinkles

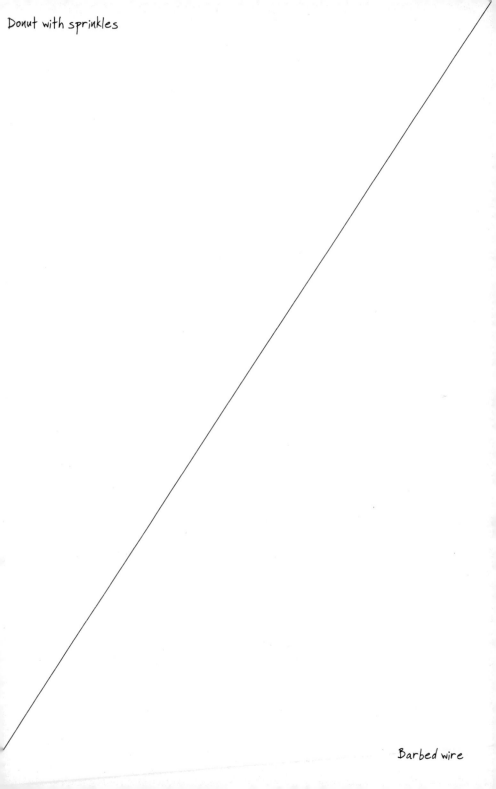

Barbed wire

Treasure map

Pirate ship

Nautical scene

Princess tiara

Sombrero

Fedora

Fireman's helmet

Mandala

Oil rig

Spinal cord

Wheel of fortune

Layers of the Earth

Drawbridge and moat

Chariot

Phoenix rising

Wrecking ball

Phone booth

Egyptian pharaoh

Exit sign

---

Old pocket watch

Cocoon metamorphosis

Brick wall

Tire swing

Perfect garden

Ball and chain

Dove

Henna tattooed hand

Cowboy boots

---

Moccasins

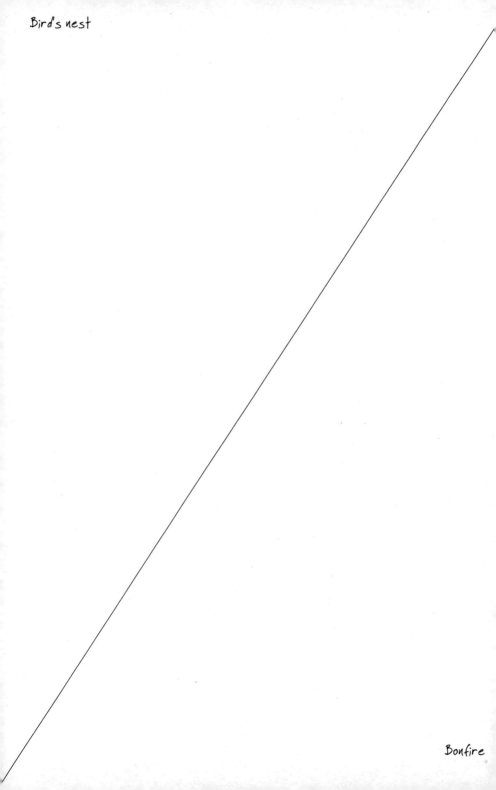

Bird's nest

Bonfire

Aquarium

Battleship

Army tank

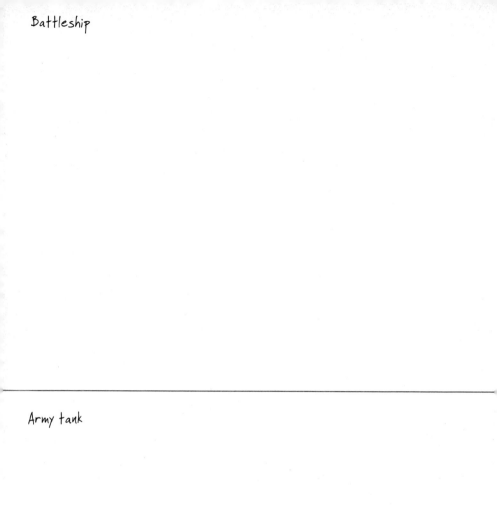

Dungeon

Dragonfly

---

Tarantula

Carnival

Crocodile

---

Catfish

Twilight zone

Mansion

Jester's hat

King's crown

Spartan

Trojan horse

Haunted house

Box of crayons

Megaphone

Mohawk

Candelabra

Dream car

---

Rainy day

Tugboat

---

Ship's anchor

Dreamcatcher

Cobra head

---

Rusty truck

Potato head man

Cheshire cat

Polka dot bow tie

---

Party hat

Barracuda

---

Piranha

Coffin

Scary shadow

Maze

Conch shell

Great white shark teeth

Utopia

Brass scuba helmet

Lobster

Cherry blossoms

---

Park bench

Hula dancer

Slice of pie

Something bohemian

Something bursting into flames

Chandelier

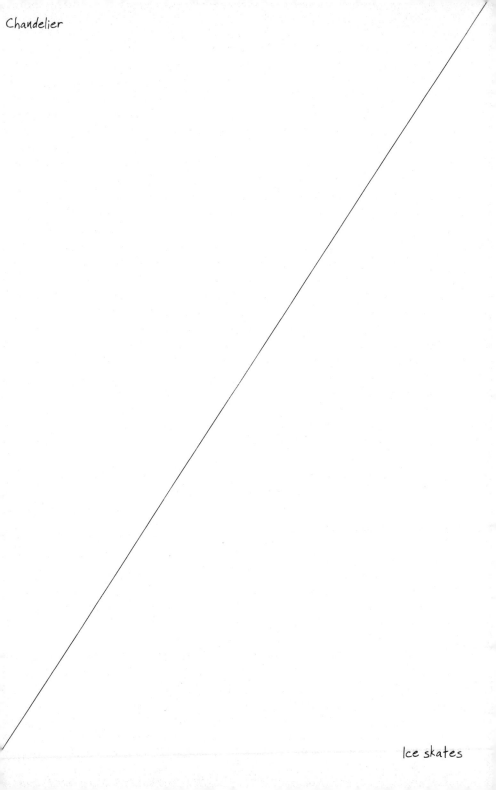

Ice skates

Tree roots underground

Locket

---

Class ring

Kimono

Nerdy glasses

Solar system

Fireflies

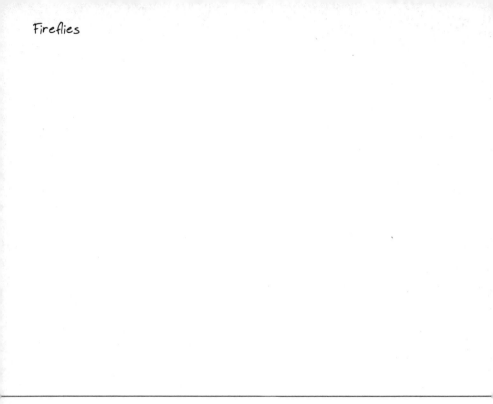

Witch's brew

Wooden clogs

---

Cassette tape

Celtic design

Boomerang

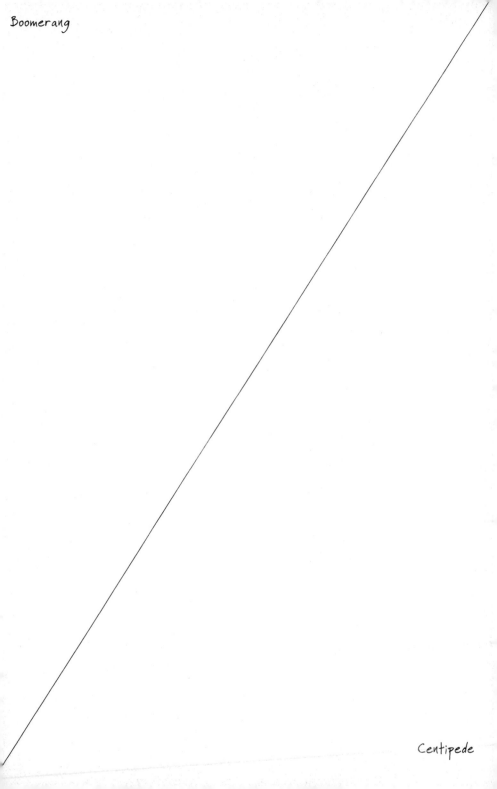

Centipede

Dark alleyway

Locomotive

Something imaginary

Baseball diamond

Leprechaun

Internal clock mechanisms

---

Santa's sled

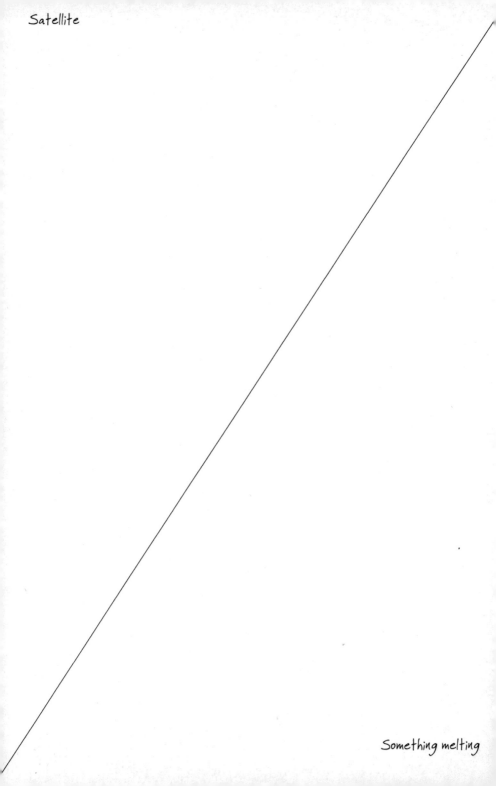

Satellite

Something melting

Palace

Padlock

---

Dart board

Factory

Inside your refrigerator

First place ribbon

Quilted blanket

Maracas

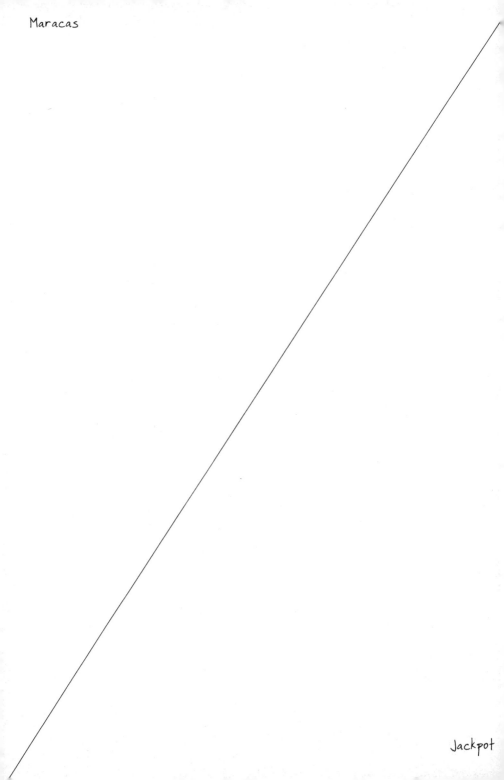

Jackpot

Star constellations

A nightmare

Tiger claws

Titanic

Your favorite logo

---

Famous sign

Rastafarian

Laboratory

The Abyss

Poker chips

Loaf of bread

Wild animals

Phases of the moon

Roulette wheel

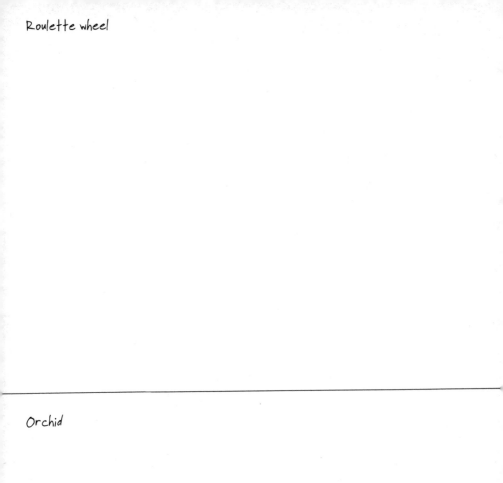

Orchid

Biplane

---

Banana split

Laughing donkey

Something funny

Your closet

Dream house

Kaleidoscope

New cartoon character

Time capsule

Panda bear

Something futuristic

UFO

Postage stamp

Crow's nest on a pirate ship

Purple people eater

Sunset

---

Coat of arms

Excited face

---

Lucky dice

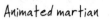
Animated martian

Circus tent

---

Skyline